Piano Exam Pieces

ABRSM Grade 8

Selected from the 2023 & 2024 syllabus

Name

Date of exam

C000054245

Contents

page

Editor for ABRSM: Richard Jones

This book includes audio recordings of all 39 pieces on the Grade 8 syllabus.
To download, please visit shop.abrsm.org/audioredeem and enter the code printed on the inside back cover.

The pieces listed above are just a selection of those on the syllabus that you can choose for your exam; the other options are listed on page 2.

Whether you are taking an ABRSM Practical or Performance Grade, pieces are at the heart of your exam; after all, playing an instrument is all about exploring, performing, and learning through repertoire.

While this book contains nine pieces in a range of styles, the full syllabus has a wealth of other exciting repertoire that we encourage you to explore – to find pieces that really inspire you, that you connect with musically and will enjoy learning, and that will allow you to perform to your very best. You can pick a mixture of pieces from this book and the wider lists if you like – you just need to have one piece from each list, A, B and C.

If you are taking a **Performance Grade**, you also need to prepare a fourth piece which is entirely your own choice. Here you have even more freedom to choose music that really speaks to you, that you want to communicate to others, and that successfully completes your programme. It can be from the syllabus lists, or somewhere else entirely. Just be sure to check the 'Selecting Repertoire' section of the Performance Grades syllabus for important requirements and options for the own-choice piece (like standard and minimum length) and the programme of four pieces overall. Finally, you need to decide what order to play your pieces in and how you, the performer, will take your audience from the very first to the very last note, including moving from one piece to another, so that the performance forms a complete musical journey.

The separate syllabuses are available at **www.abrsm.org**. Whether taking a Practical or Performance Grade, enjoy exploring the possibilities on offer!

First published in 2022 by ABRSM (Publishing) Ltd,
a wholly owned subsidiary of ABRSM, 4 London Wall Place,
London EC2Y 5AU, United Kingdom
© 2022 by The Associated Board of the Royal Schools of Music
Distributed worldwide by Oxford University Press

Music origination by Julia Bovee
Cover by Lloyd Winters, Kate Benjamin & Andy Potts, with thanks to
Trinity School, Croydon
Printed in England by Caligraving Ltd, Thetford, Norfolk, on materials
from sustainable sources. P15727

Piano Exam Pieces
2023 & 2024

Other pieces for Grade 8

		Composer	Piece	Publication
A	4	J. S. Bach	Prelude and Fugue in G, BWV 884	J. S. Bach: The Well-Tempered Clavier, Part 2 (ABRSM)
	5	Beethoven	Allegro (1st movt from *Sonata in E*, Op.14 No.1)	Beethoven: Sonata in E, Op.14 No.1 (ABRSM) *or* Beethoven: The 35 Piano Sonatas, Vol. 1 (ABRSM) *or* Beethoven: Complete Pianoforte Sonatas, Vol. 1 (ABRSM)
	6	Handel	Prelude **and** Allegro (Fuga) (1st **and** 2nd movts from *Suite No. 8 in F minor*, HWV 433)	Handel: Eight Great Suites, Book 2 (ABRSM) *or* Handel: Keyboard Works, Vol. 1 (Bärenreiter)
	7	Martínez	Allegro/Moderato (1st movt from *Sonata in A*)	Piano Music by Female Composers (4th revised edition 2011) (Schott) *or* Core Classics, Grades 7–8 (ABRSM)
	8	Mozart	Andante grazioso **and** Vars. 1–6 (1st movt from *Sonata in A*, K.331)	Mozart: Sonata in A, K.331 (ABRSM) *or* Mozart: Sonatas for Pianoforte, Vol. 2 (ABRSM)
	9	Rameau	Les cyclopes (from *Pièces de clavecin*)	Rameau: Les cyclopes / Les sauvages (Bärenreiter) *or* Rameau: Pièces de clavecin (Heugel)
	10	D. Scarlatti	Sonata in D, Kp. 443, L. 418	Pp. 4–7 from D. Scarlatti: Selected Keyboard Sonatas, Book 1 (ABRSM) *or* D. Scarlatti: 200 Sonatas, Vol. 4 (EMB Zeneműkiadó)
	11	Haydn	Allegro con brio (1st movt from *Sonata in D*, Hob. XVI:37)	Haydn: Selected Keyboard Sonatas, Book 3 (ABRSM) *or* Haydn: Complete Piano Sonatas, Vol. 3 (Wiener Urtext)
	12	Stephen Hough	Toccatina (5th movt from *Suite R-B*)	Stephen Hough: Suite R-B and Other Enigmas (Weinberger)
	13	C. Schumann	Un poco agitato (No. 2 from *Quatre pièces fugitives*, Op.15)	C. Schumann: Romantic Piano Music (Vol. 2) (Bärenreiter) *or* C. Schumann: Quatre pièces fugitives Op.15 (Breitkopf & Härtel)
B	4	Arensky	Nocturne in Db (No. 3 from *24 Characteristic Pieces*, Op. 36)	Arensky: 24 Characteristic Pieces, Op. 36 (Prhythm) *or* Arensky: 24 Morceau characteristiques, Op. 36 (Alfred)
	5	Chopin	Mazurka in A minor, Op.17 No. 4	Chopin: Mazurkas (Henle)
	6	Ireland	Columbine	Ireland: The Collected Piano Works, Vol. 4 (Stainer & Bell)
	7	Janáček	Andante (No.1 from *In the Mists*)	Janáček: In the Mists (Bärenreiter)
	8	Rachmaninoff	Moment musical in Db, Op.16 No. 5	Rachmaninoff: Six moments musicaux, Op.16 (Simrock)
	9	Schubert	Impromptu in Ab (No. 2 from *Four Impromptus*, Op.142, D.935)	Schubert: Impromptus, Op.142 (ABRSM) *or* Schubert: Impromptus and Moments musicaux (Henle) *or* Core Classics, Grades 7–8 (ABRSM)
	10	Schumann	Romanze in F♯ (No. 2 from *Drei Romanzen*, Op. 28)	Schumann: Drei Romanzen, Op. 28 (ABRSM)
	11	A. Beach	A Hermit Thrush at Morn, Op. 92 No. 2	Piano Music of Amy Beach (Hal Leonard) *or* Amy Beach Piano Music (Dover)
	12	Beethoven	Adagio cantabile (2nd movt from *Sonata in C minor 'Pathétique'*, Op.13)	Beethoven: Sonata in C minor, Op.13 (Pathétique) (ABRSM) *or* Beethoven: The 35 Piano Sonatas, Vol. 1 (ABRSM) *or* Beethoven: Complete Pianoforte Sonatas, Vol. 1 (ABRSM)
	13	Tailleferre	Impromptu	Tailleferre: Impromptu (Editions Jobert)
C	4	Chaminade	Pierrette (Air de Ballet), Op. 41	Piano Music by Female Composers (4th revised edition 2011) (Schott)
	5	Chen Peixun	Thunder in Drought Season	100 Years of Chinese Piano Music: Vol. III Works in Traditional Style, Book II Instrumental Music (Shanghai Conservatory of Music Press)
	6	Debussy	Rêverie	Debussy: Rêverie (Editions Jobert) *or* Night and Dreams (Schott)
	7	Khachaturian	Toccata	Khachaturian: Toccata (Boosey & Hawkes)
	8	Uwe Korn	Caballos Españoles	Tango Meets Jazz (Schott)
	9	Cecilia McDowall	Vespers in Venice (from *Four Piano Solos*)	Cecilia McDowall: Four Piano Solos (Hunt Edition)
	10	Villa-Lobos	O polichinelo (from *A prole do bebê no.1*)	Villa-Lobos: O polichinelo (Eschig) *or* Beyond the Romantic Spirit, Book 2 (Alfred)
	11	Bartók	Dance in Bulgarian Rhythm No. 6 (No.153 from *Mikrokosmos*)	Bartók: Six Dances in Bulgarian Rhythm (Henle) *or* Bartók: Mikrokosmos, Vol. 6 (Boosey & Hawkes)
	12	Zoe Rahman	Go with the Flow	Nikki Iles and Friends, Book 2 (ABRSM)
	13	Trad. Irish	Danny Boy, arr. Iles	Jazz in Autumn (OUP)

Prelude and Fugue in B flat

BWV 866

No. 21 from *Das wohltemperirte Clavier*, Part I

J. S. Bach
(1685–1750)

This Prelude and Fugue is taken from Bach's *Das wohltemperirte Clavier* (Well-Tempered Clavier), Part I (Cöthen, 1722), a set of 24 preludes and fugues in all keys, arranged in chromatic order. The title refers to the type of tuning that would make it possible to play in all keys – equal temperament, or something close to it.

In the toccata-style prelude, the big chords in bar 11 are marked 'Adagio' in the copy of a Bach pupil. This would also apply to the similar chords in bars 13, 15–16 and 17–18, whereas the linking runs return to the original fast tempo. The sprightly fugue is notable for its triple counterpoint – passages in which three themes are joined together in different vertical combinations (bars 9, 13, etc.).

Source: autograph MS, Staatsbibliothek zu Berlin, Preussischer Kulturbesitz, Mus. ms. Bach P 415

© 1994 by The Associated Board of the Royal Schools of Music
Adapted from J. S. Bach: *The Well-Tempered Clavier*, Part I, edited by Richard Jones (ABRSM)

Prelude

[♩ = c.58]

Fugue

[♩ = c.72]

A:2

Allegro

First movement from Sonata in F, K. 332

W. A. Mozart
(1756–91)

Mozart's three piano sonatas K. 330–332 are among his most popular keyboard works. They were composed in the period 1781–3, possibly during a visit to Salzburg. In view of Mozart's flair for opera, it is not surprising that this Allegro is operatic in its sudden changes of mood, from the gently lyrical (starting at bars 1 and 41) to the stormy (bars 22 and 56).

In the late 18th century, the wedge sign (bars 15, 24, etc.) indicated staccato, an accent or both. The grace notes in bars 25, 37 and 41–42 etc. should start on the beat, not before.

Sources: autograph MS, Scheide Library, Princeton, NJ (USA); first edition: no. 3 of *Trois sonates pour le clavecin ou pianoforte*, *Oeuvre VI* (Vienna: Artaria, 1784)

© 1982 by The Associated Board of the Royal Schools of Music
Adapted from Mozart: *Sonatas for Pianoforte*, Vol. II, edited by Stanley Sadie and Denis Matthews (ABRSM)

Moment musical in C sharp minor

No. 4 from *Moments musicaux*, D. 780

Franz Schubert
(1797–1828)

For Schubert, the piano – his main instrument – was 'the vehicle of the most personal, intimate expression', to quote his biographer Alfred Einstein. This is certainly true of the short, lyrical pieces of his last years – the Impromptus and the *Moments musicaux*. No. 4 in C sharp minor from this collection, in its outer sections, is similar to certain preludes from Bach's *Well-Tempered Clavier*, whereas the middle section in D flat major is more dance-like.

Howard Ferguson, editor of the ABRSM edition, points out that the pedal sign in bar 22, 2nd beat, should probably be under beat 1 (the same applies in bar 123).

Source: first complete edition, *Momens musicals* [sic] *pour le Piano Forte, Oeuvre 94* (Vienna: Leidesdorf, [1828])

© 1983 by The Associated Board of the Royal Schools of Music
Adapted from Schubert: *Moments musicaux*, edited by Howard Ferguson (ABRSM)

Moderato [♩ = c.88]

22

B:1

Impromptu in B minor

No. 2 from Two Impromptus

Samuel Coleridge-Taylor
(1875–1912)

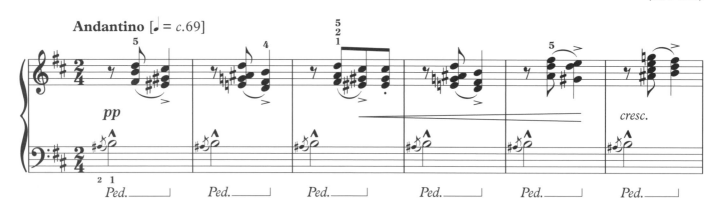

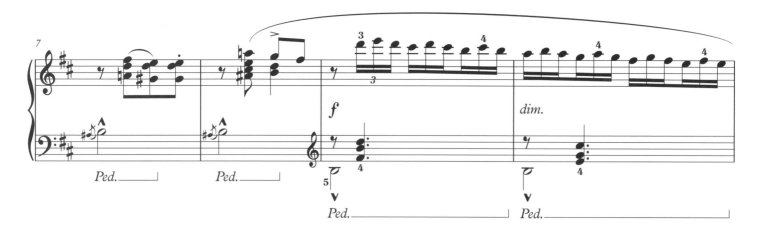

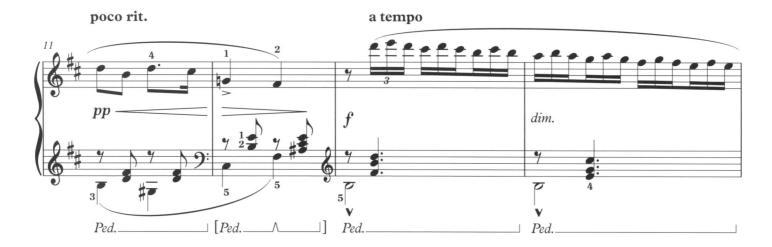

Samuel Coleridge-Taylor was an English composer, conductor and composition teacher. As a young composer he was much influenced by Dvořák, and he became famous for his cantata *Hiawatha's Wedding Feast*. In later life, inspired by poet Paul Laurence Dunbar, he became increasingly interested in aspects of his African heritage. This is reflected in compositions such as *African Romances*, *African Suite* and *Four African Dances*.

'Impromptu' is a title used by Schubert, Schumann, Chopin and others. It is French for 'without preparation' and implies a spontaneous approach to composition, relying on sudden inspiration. Like many impromptus, this one is in ternary form (ABA), with the middle section B starting at bar 45 and the varied return of A at bar 89.

Sources: first edition, *Two Impromptus* (London: Augener, 1911); *Impromptu II* (London: Stainer & Bell, n.d.). The latter is a corrected edition with fingering added.

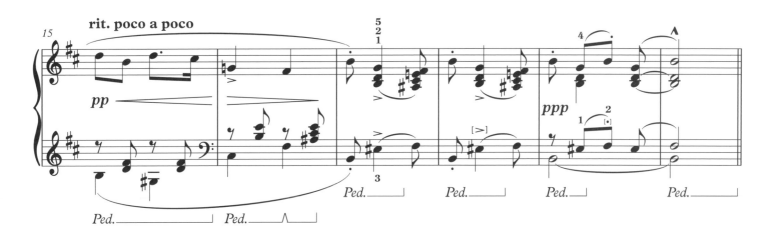

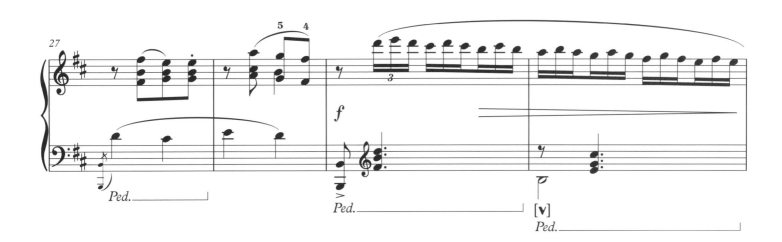

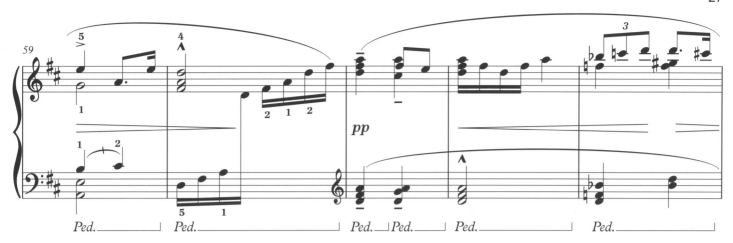

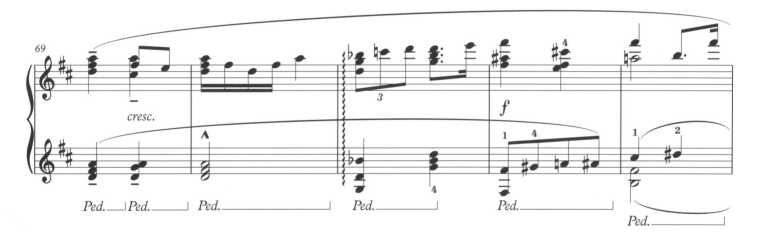

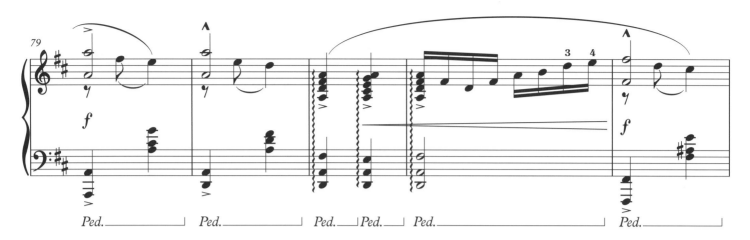

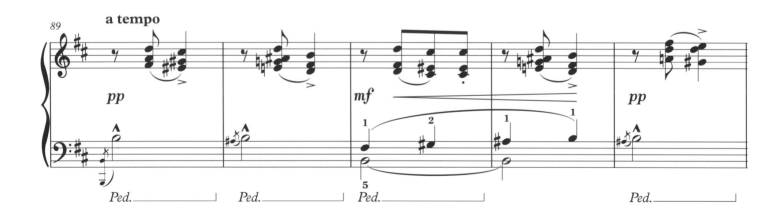

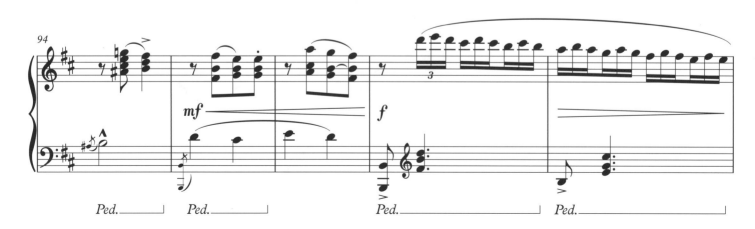

B:2

Étude in D flat

Op. 41 No. 5

Louise Farrenc
(1804–75)

The French pianist Louise Farrenc composed many piano and chamber-music pieces, and was professor of piano at the Paris Conservatoire for over 30 years. She and her husband edited a 23-volume anthology of early keyboard music, *Le trésor des pianistes* (The Pianist's Treasure).

This piece is in ternary form (ABA), which was common in song-like piano pieces in the 19th century. The melodious A section in D flat major (bars 1–29) is followed by a passionate middle section in C sharp minor (the tonic minor, bars 30–59), after which the A section returns (bars 60–88), plus a brief coda (bars 88–94). Although the composer's metronome marks are ♪ = 108 and ♪ = 120, students may prefer slower tempos, for example ♪ = *c*.100 and ♪ = *c*.112 respectively.

Sources: first edition, *12 études brillantes*, Op. 41 (Paris: l'auteur, n.d.); later edition, *12 études de dexterité*, Op. 41 (Paris: Leduc, n.d. [1876]). The music text of the two editions appears to be identical. In bar 60, **a tempo** has been altered by the editor to **Tempo Primo**.

Juin: Barcarolle

No. 6 from *Les saisons*, Op. 37b

B:3

P. I. Tchaikovsky
(1840–93)

Les saisons (The Seasons) was commissioned by N. M. Bernard, publisher of *La Nouvelliste*, a musical journal from St Petersburg, Russia. In 1876, Bernard asked Tchaikovsky to write a piano piece for each month, illustrating its poetic character in his music. Tchaikovsky was guided in the composition of each piece by an epigram from a Russian poet. At the end of 1876 Bernard published the 12 pieces in a collection entitled *Les saisons* – a strange title for a work about the months of the year.

 'Juin' (June) is subtitled 'Barcarolle' – a song of the Venetian gondoliers. The epigram for this month is: 'Let us go to the shore; there the waves will kiss our feet. With mysterious sadness the stars will shine down on us'.

Sources: autograph MS, Russian National Museum of Music, Moscow; *Oeuvres complètes pour le piano, nouvelle edition revue par l'auteur*, Vol. 3 (Moscow & Leipzig: P. Jürgenson [1890])

C:1

Rumores de La Caleta

Malagueña

No. 6 from *Recuerdos de viaje*, Op. 71

Isaac Albéniz
(1860–1909)

The Spanish (Catalan) composer Isaac Albéniz was a child prodigy as a pianist – he gave public concerts from the age of about five. Today he is best known as a composer of piano music, coloured by the rhythms and harmonies of Spanish folk-dance music. The early *Rumores de La Caleta* (Murmurs from La Caleta), from the collection *Recuerdos de viaje* (Travel Impressions), imitates the Spanish guitar, which is interrupted by *cantando* passages for 'solo soprano' at bars 26 and 44, and above all in the relative-major middle section (bars 72–95) of this ABA piece. 'La Caleta' is the name of a beach in the Andalusian region of Spain.

Source: *Recuerdos de viaje*, Op. 71 (Paris: Union musicale Franco-Espagnole, 1929)

C:2

Arabesque No. 2

from *Deux arabesques*, L. 66

Claude Debussy
(1862–1918)

The French composer Claude Debussy wrote what many people regard as the most original piano music since Chopin. This Arabesque is an early piece, but we already find here the impressionist tendencies and the lightness of touch which are hallmarks of Debussy's later works. The title 'arabesque', previously used by Schumann, refers to the florid, decorative nature of the musical material.

Sources: autograph MS, Bibliothèque nationale de France; *Deux Arabesques* (Paris: Durand, 1904)

Drive

Over the Bars

J. P. Johnson
(1894–1955)

James Price Johnson was an American pianist and composer who was influenced by the ragtime of Scott Joplin and became a major figure in the early years of jazz. He was a stride pianist – striding with his left hand between bass notes and chords – and many others followed his example, including Fats Waller and Duke Ellington.

Over the Bars is a typical example of a stride piano piece. The striding can accompany very different right-hand parts – compare, for example, the section starting at bar 9 with the Drive at bars 41 and 69. The piece contains no dynamics beyond those of the final Drive (bar 69), so players should add their own dynamic scheme.